The Cake Machine

By Paul Shipton
Illustrated by Steve Cox

Contents

- The Cake Machine 2
- Picture Dictionary 14
- About **Read and Imagine** 16

Grandpa and Clunk go to the shop in the van.

Grandpa looks for eggs and milk.

'Can you see strawberries, Clunk?' he asks.

Can you see strawberries, Clunk?

In the kitchen, Ben and Rosie see the shopping bags.

'Do you like cake?' asks Grandpa.

'Yes!' say Ben and Rosie.

Do you like cake?

'Can you make a cake, Grandpa?' asks Rosie.

'Yes, I can,' says Grandpa. 'This is my new machine. It's a Cake Machine!'

Grandpa puts eggs, flour, and butter in the machine.

Then Clunk puts in sugar and strawberries.

Grandpa counts, 'Three, two, one …'

'A big, red cake!' says Grandpa.

A cake comes out. It isn't big and red. It's small and black.

'We can't eat this!' says Ben.

'Let's make a new cake,' says Grandpa.
Ben and Rosie watch the Cake Machine.

'Three, two, one …' Grandpa counts.
There is no cake.
'Where is it?' asks Ben.
Grandpa looks at the machine.
He hits it with his hand.

Mum, Ben and Rosie go to a café.

They have a big, red, strawberry ice cream cake!

Grandpa and Clunk don't go to the café.

They're in the kitchen.

'I like this cake!' says Clunk.

 # Picture Dictionary

ask

butter

café

cake

count

eat

egg

flour

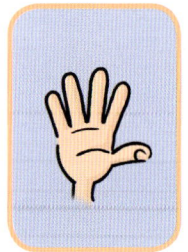
hand

hit

ice cream

kitchen

 look for

 machine

 milk

 shop

 shopping bags

 strawberries

 sugar

 van

Oxford Read and Imagine

Oxford Read and Imagine graded readers are at nine levels (Early Starter, Starter, Beginner, and Levels 1 to 6) for students from age 3 or 4 and older. They offer great stories to read and enjoy.

At Levels 1 to 6, every storybook reader links to an **Oxford Read and Discover** non-fiction reader, giving students a chance to find out more about the world around them, and an opportunity for Content and Language Integrated Learning (CLIL).

For more information about **Read and Imagine**, and for Teacher's Notes, go to www.oup.com/elt/teacher/readandimagine

For a free Audio download of the story in a choice of American and British English, go to www.oup.com/elt/readandimagine

OXFORD
UNIVERSITY PRESS

Great Clarendon Street, Oxford, OX2 6DP, United Kingdom

Oxford University Press is a department of the University of Oxford. It furthers the University's objective of excellence in research, scholarship, and education by publishing worldwide. Oxford is a registered trade mark of Oxford University Press in the UK and in certain other countries

© Oxford University Press 2019

The moral rights of the author have been asserted

First published in 2019

2023 2022 2021 2020

10 9 8

No unauthorized photocopying

All rights reserved. No part of this publication may be reproduced, stored in a retrieval system, or transmitted, in any form or by any means, without the prior permission in writing of Oxford University Press, or as expressly permitted by law, by licence or under terms agreed with the appropriate reprographics rights organization.

Enquiries concerning reproduction outside the scope of the above should be sent to the ELT Rights Department, Oxford University Press, at the address above

You must not circulate this work in any other form and you must impose this same condition on any acquirer

Links to third party websites are provided by Oxford in good faith and for information only. Oxford disclaims any responsibility for the materials contained in any third party website referenced in this work

ISBN: 978 0 19 416743 7

Printed in China

This book is printed on paper from certified and well-managed sources

ACKNOWLEDGEMENTS

Main illustrations by: Steve Cox.

Activity illustrations by: Dusan Pavlic/Beehive Illustration, Alan Rowe, Mark Ruffle.